# EVIL PLANS AND STUFF

Made in United States
Orlando, FL
22 June 2023

34391367R00070